THE GOOD BOOK TO THE LAKES

by

HUNTER DAVIES

Yes — but what the hell is it?

Published by Forster Davies Ltd, Caldbeck, Cumbria

Published by Forster Davies Ltd, Caldbeck, Cumbria

Giant's grave, Penrith.

The Good Quiz Book to the Lakes by Hunter Davies.

First published in G.B. 1987 by Forster Davies Ltd, Caldbeck, Cumbria.

Made and printed in Cumbria by Frank Peters Colour Printers, Gatebeck, Kendal, Cumbria.

Distributed by Century Hutchinson, 62, Chandos Place, London, WC2. All trade orders to Tiptree Book Services, Tiptree, Essex, CD5 0SR. Tel 0621-816362

ISBN 0 9509 190 3 9

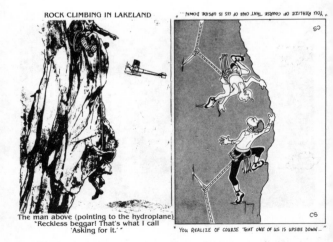

ROCK CLIMBING IN LAKELAND

The man above (pointing to the hydroplane)
"Reckless beggar! That's what I call
'Asking for it.' "

" YOU REALIZE OF COURSE THAT ONE OF US IS UPSIDE DOWN ... "

Fifty years of Lakeland Funny Postcards: One from the 1980's and one from the 1930's. Guess which.

CONTENTS

𝕿hree guesses — where am 𝕴?

Crummock Water.

3

Introduction

THE GOOD QUIZ BOOK TO THE LAKES

Every time I've come back from the Lake District over the years, zooming down the rotten old M6 towards London, I've subjected the family to a quiz. Oh, pretty easy stuff at first, especially when they were all young. Come on now, Flora, tell me two Lakeland towns beginning with K. Okay, Jake, as you're so clever, tell me three mountains over 3,000 feet. And for you Caitlin, I want the sixteen lakes, in order of size. That usually kept them quiet, till the next Motorway Service Station. What am I saying? We don't usually stop at vulgar Service Stations, apart from getting petrol. We try to drive off into the rural byways, find a nice quiet place, commune with nature, and have a picnic. Sometimes that can take absolutely ages. No wonder our journeys home last so long. No wonder I play all those boring I mean terribly interesting quiz games, just to keep them occupied.

I also ask them questions on what we personally have done in the Lakes on that particular trip. Oh, I dunno. Silly things really. What sort of people sat next to us in that cafe in Ambleside and what were they talking about? How many were on top of Scafell when we got there? Was it a man or a woman in charge of Gondola and what was he or she wearing?

Then, as we finally near home, we do our Best Day of the Holiday Survey. This is an opinion poll, not a quiz. Flora, being the youngest, reads out from my diary the details of what we did each day and we give it marks out of ten for sheer pleasure. She then tots up all the marks. This used to last for miles and miles and lead to lots of arguments.

When we started this family game, calculators had not been invented. She then announces, tum tee tum, the answers in reverse order, just like the Miss World contest. She tells us the least enjoyed days and then finishes with the Top Three Most Enjoyed Days by the Davies Family During Their Lakeland Hol. I have all the results somewhere, stretching back for years and years. The winner was usually a terrific climb in the sun, followed by a brilliant meal in the evening. All pretty obvious stuff.

As they got older, the bigger ones often moaned about Hunt's stupid quiz, and his silly questions and dopey polls, well you know what teenagers are like, but in the end they usually joined in. Such things do help to fill up time on a long journey.

I leave you to work out your own family questions, and arrange opinion polls to suit your personal tastes and experiences, but I thought I might humbly offer a general quiz on Lakeland, for all people who might be about to have a trip to the Lakes, or just had one, or only be thinking in their armchairs about Lakeland.

Today, thirteen million people visit the Lakes every year, an incredible amount, but even more remarkable is the latest research which shows that 90% come by car. So, folks, here is some car fodder, all about Lakeland. That should keep them quiet.

It's arranged under ten sections, dealing with nine different aspects of Lakeland life, from Lakes to Literature, Mountains to Museums. The tenth section is Fun and Games. You can do it on your own, or have one person read out all the questions. Then check the answers at the back, after everyone has had a go. I've tried to keep the framework simple, as I envisage many people doing the quiz on the move. Please, please do not try any of the picture questions on the driver, not when he or she is actually driving. I do want you all to get home safely.

It's terribly childish in parts, and aren't we all, and other times it's pretty tough, aren't we all.It is meant to cover a range of abilities and interests, for complete beginners, as well as those with specialised Lakeland knowledge. You could learn a lot from this little book. You never know when it might come in handy, at school, at work, or next time you're on television. I was asked not long ago by the BBC to compile a set of questions for Mastermind. (The contestant got them almost all correct. I must try harder.) Why not make Lakeland **your** special subject, just in case? There are so many pubs these days where they have general knowledge leagues and competitions, and of course the success of Trivial Pursuits shows that the whole world is becoming question and answer mad. Or just trivia mad.

You could organise your own game out of this book, letting contestants choose their own section, from 1-10, then picking a number, 1-50, out of a hat to see which question in each section they have to answer. But you're clever. You can work something out on your own. In fact, I'm amazed you've bought this book. You could have done your own. You looked the intelligent sort from the moment you picked up this book. I said as much to the wife.

Please don't cheat and look up the answers before you have exhaused yourself and everyone else. It will help if you have actually been to the Lakes, and kept your eyes and ears open. It will also have done you an enormous power of good if you have read one of the excellent modern guide books on Lakeland. I'm thinking especially of "The Good Guide to the Lakes", an absolutely brilliant and marvellous and original book. It gets up-dated and revised every two years, for ever and ever, so don't miss it. It will make an excellent crib, as it's an invaluable guide to everything in Lakeland.

This little offering is not meant to be invaluable. Just an amusement. Have a pleasant wander through it. And a safe journey home . . .

Hunter Davies,
January, 1987.

General Information

If you think this section looks too boring to start on, then skip to a more interesting looking bit. I don't mind. I'm not proud. It's here to establish some basic stuff about Lakeland, just to test exactly what you know about the wonderful world of our greatest National Park, our greatest Natural Treasure. Absolute Beginners, as well as Clever Clogs, could learn a lot. If you have decided to belt on, come back later. I'll be waiting . . .

National Parks

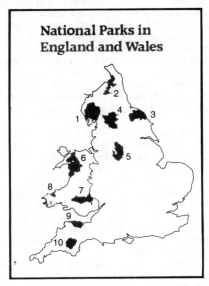

National Parks in England and Wales

1 Quite an easy one, but I want correct names, please. Here's a map of ten National Parks, numbered one to ten. Name them.

1

2

3

4

5

6

7

8

9

10

2 A bit harder, but rather pretty. Here are the symbols for the ten National Parks. You must have recognized the Lake District one at least. Name them.

3 The first sorts of National Parks anywhere were set up in 1872. In which country? France: Germany: USA: New Zealand: or Britain.

Lake District National Park

4 The Lake District National Park was set up in: 1901: 1931: or 1951.

5 The Lake District National Park is the biggest in England and Wales. Does it cover approximately: 80 square miles: 880 square miles: or 8,000 square miles.

6 What does LDSPB stand for?

7 The NP Rangers wear special uniforms. What do their jumpers look like?

8 Which of these Cumbrian towns is **not** in the NP: Grasmere, Kendal, Keswick, Caldbeck, Cockermouth, Penrith, Ambleside.

9 Where is the HQ of the National Park?

10 Two of these slogans have been used in recent years by the Cumbria Tourist Board, but one of them I've just made up. Which?
a) "The Lake District — a place for all seasons"
b) "English Lakeland — the most beautiful corner of England"
c) "Lakeland — the very roots of Heaven"

Driving

11 Name the pass and the Inn.

12 You're driving up the M6 from the south, what's the first Junction number you come to in Cumbria?

13 Take this more carefully: coming from the south, what's the first Motorway Junction in the National Park?

14 Coming from Scotland, what number is the first Junction you join on the M6?

15 Driving at 60 mph which is quite sufficient, how long do you think it would take to drive through Cumbria on the dreaded M6, from the southern boundary line to the end of the Motorway at Carlisle?

16 Name the A road between Kendal and Windermere. (I don't mean Hellish. I mean what number is it?)

17 What number is the A road between Grasmere and Keswick?

18 You're on the A592, having left Penrith, heading southish. What's the first lake you come to on your left-hand side?

19 Keep on going, still on the A592, what's the big lake you eventually come to on your right?

20 Coming south from Cockermouth on the B5289, what's the first lake you pass on the right?

21 You're stuck in Sellafield, poor you, and want the quickest route to Ambleside. What two passes would you cross?

22 You're in Kendal, getting fed up with the one-way system. Does the traffic go north to south, or south to north along Highgate?

23 You're driving north to Keswick, wondering if you have too many people on board. What's that lake behind?

Railways

24 Which of these have working railway stations: Penrith, Keswick, Kendal, Cockermouth.

25 You're on the main Intercity line — where would you change for the branch line to Windermere?

26 You're trying to get to Barrow quickly, as you've heard it's terribly attractive. Where do you branch off on the main railway line, coming from the south?

27 There was a line which connected Cockermouth, Keswick and Penrith, but it closed in 1972. What was the name of the railway company which originally ran it?

28 Now a really hard one, for railway buffs. Carlisle can boast it used to have seven different railway companies running into the town, a record equalled only by York. Can you name three at least?

Cumbria

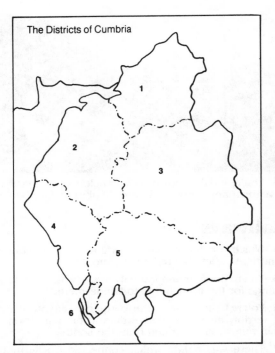

The Districts of Cumbria

29 Cumbria is divided into six District Councils. Name them.

30 Which is the County town of Cumbria?

31 Westmorland is no more. Which was its County town?

32 From which towns are the following newspapers produced: a Cumberland News: b Westmorland Gazette: c West Cumberland Times & Star.

33 Who publishes the Lake District Guardian?

34 Where is the NP's Visitor Centre?

35 Arrange in order of size the largest landowner in the NP: National Park Authority: National Trust: Forestry Commission.

36 What's the population of Cumbria, to the nearest 10,000?

37 What's the population of the National Park?

38 Where would you say most visitors to Lakeland came from — North east England: North west England: or London and the South east.

39 If you see the letters HH on a car number plate, which town should it be from?

History and Geography

40 Where was Luguvallium?

41 When was Hadrian's Wall begun?

42 Where is the end of Hadrian's Wall in Cumbria?

43 What does beck mean?

44 What was the Celtic name for Cumbria?

45 What were statesmen?

46 What was Kendal Green?

47 Where did Edward I die and where is his Monument?

Phone Numbers

48 If you rang these phone numbers what would you get?
a Windermere 5151: b Windermere 4444: c Kendal 24555: d Carlisle 23456.

49 Which towns lie behind these phone codes:
a 07687: b 0539: c 096 65: d 085 36.

50 You've had an accident. What number do you dial to call out a Mountain Rescue Team?

Section Two

Hotels, Pubs, Eating and Drinking

If you haven't actually been to the Lake District this section could prove a trifle hard. You'll have to do a hell of a lot of guessing. But if you have stayed there, in a posh hotel or just a tent, had a few meals and wandered round, or simply read the advertisements and leaflets, then come on, it should be rather easy . . .

1 Name the two hotels above.

2 Still looking at the same two hotels, can you guess the prices? At which one would you expect in 1987 to pay the following amounts, on average, for dinner bed and breakfast?
a £60 at least: b Not much more than £20.

3 How many hotels are there in Lakeland: 75: 750: 7,500.

4 Which hotel did Brian Sack and Francis Coulson open on Ullswater?

5 What's the name of the hotel John Tovey created?

6 Which hotel boasts that it is Lakeland's biggest hotel?

7 In which towns are the following hotels:
a The Belsfield: b The Beech Hill: c Rothay Manor.

8 What's the correct name — the Swiss Lodore Hotel or the Lodore Swiss Hotel: and where is it?

9 Uplands is a branch of a famous hotel — which one — and where is it?

10 Name the hotel in Keswick which has stained glass portraits in memory of the Lake Poets.

11 Where's the Three Shires Inn?

12 Where's the Twa Dogs Inn?

13 Two old postcards of Lakeland hotels, still going strong. Name them.

14 You're driving north from Keswick on the A591, and you've just passed Bass Lake. What's the big hotel on the left, at the cross-roads?

Restaurants

Saturday, 19th November, 1983.

DINNER

Sharrow Home-made Speciality Soups:- Cream of Mushroom : Game Soup : Hollandaise Vegetable :
Simple Beef Consomme : Sharrow Brioche with Chicken Liver Pate (hot speciality) :
Beignets de Fromage (cheese choux puffs) : Biscuit de Poisson (hot fish terrine) :
Dariole of Game Mousseline, served with Calvados Sauce (another hot speciality) :
Quiche Divan (broccoli, chicken, and gruyere cheese) : Avocado Mousse & Dressed Prawns :
Fresh Crayfish cooked in a reduction of White Wine & Cream, with Tarragon & Vegetables :
Game Terrine served with Cumberland Sauce : Mushrooms cooked in Garlic Butter :
Fresh Salmon, marinated in Walnut Oil, Lemon Juice & White Wine, with Tarragon & Vegetables :
Terrine of Halibut & Salmon Mousseline, with Hollandaise :   Shrimps in Cream Sauce :
Fresh Melon, Orange & Grapefruit Cocktail : Smoked Salmon with Avocado Mousseline :
Fine-textured Chicken Liver Parfait with Cognac, served in a small Puff Pastry Casing :
Chicken Livers cooked in Cream with Mushrooms & Marjoram : Melon in Cream Curry Sauce :
*****

15 Whose first courses?

ENGLISH LAKES

THE SELECTION OF
SWEETS TO-NIGHT INCLUDE

Chocolate Orange Cream in
Butterscotch Shortbread
Tartlet

Port and Claret Jelly with
Shortbread

Hazelnut Meringue Slice with
Fresh Guavas

Pineapple and Passion Fruit
cream Pavlova

Lemon Curd Galette Slice

Black Cherry Rum Farmhouse Pie

Strawberry Cheesecake

Calvados Apple Chocolate Crunch

Cheese Platter with Home
Made Biscuits

COFFEE IS SERVED IN THE LOUNGES, WHERE YOU MAY SMOKE

16 Whose puddings?

17 Where is Sheila's cottage?

18 Where is Roger's Restaurant?

19 Where is Jackson's Bistro?

20 Where is Passepartout?

21 Where is Zeffirellis?

22 Where is The Wordsworth Hotel?

23 Where is Michael's Nook?

24 Where is the Chaucer House Hotel?

25 At which of these literary homes can you get a meal: a Dove Cottage b Brantwood c Hill Top

26 If you're looking through the Porthole, which town are you in?

27 There must be scores, but name three towns or villages which have a Sun.

28 The Oddfellows Arms became the John Peel Inn, then in 1986 went back to its old name. Where is it?

29 What's the local brewery in Cockermouth called?

30 What's the local brewery in Ulverston?

31 What's the name of the farmhouse in Watendlath that does teas?

32 What used to happen at Maysons in Keswick?

33 Name a bookshop in Penrith that also does teas.

34 Where is: a The Mortal Man: b The Late Kings Arms.

35 Where is: a The Eagle and Child: b The Wild Boar: c The Fat Lamb.

36 What did Sarah Nelson invent?

ROMNEY'S
EVEREST
KENDAL MINT CAKE
Manufactured by
GEORGE ROMNEY, LTD. IN KENDAL.
The Gateway to the English Lakes

Romney's Kendal Mint Cake was carried to the summit of MOUNT EVEREST on 29th May, 1953. *"We sat on the snow and looked at the country far below us . . . . we nibbled Kendal Mint Cake."* A member of the successful Everest Expedition wrote—*"It was easily the most popular item on our high altitude ration—our only criticism was that we did not have enough of it."*

37 There are four main manufacturers of Kendal Mint Cake, all in Kendal — name three of them. (To make it easy, here is a clue.)

38 What do you do with Cumberland rum butter:
a Drink it?
b Spread it on a scone?
c Oil the bike with it?

39 Is a Cumberland sausage:
a A fat, silly person?
b A garment made from Herdwick wool to keep out draughts?
c A continuous piece of local sausage meat?

40 The Calvert Trust specializes in accommodation for what sort of people?

Youth Hostels

41 There are 30 Youth Hostels in Cumbria. Name these

a

b

c

d

Old Hotels

42 Somewhere in Borrowdale — name the hotel and village.

43 On Ullswater. There, that's a really good clue. Name it, and nearest hamlet.

44 This one is on the Solway. Changed hands several times in recent years, but still there, handsome as ever.

45 In which town is this pavement cafe?

46 What did the State Management used to manage?

47 Who painted this pretty picture?

48 In what book does it appear?

49 Where is the Tower Bank Arms?

50 Who owns it today?

Section Three

Towns, Villages, Hamlets

Townies should find this easy, especially the sort of folks who hardly ever get up on to the fells, what a shame, but spend a lot of their time at street level, looking for exciting things, like a pub that's open, or another slate table lamp. To make the questions harder, a lot of the accompanying photographs are old. (Well, it does save paying photographers.) But I'm sure you'll recognize most of them.

Just to test your eyes, here are three Lakeland towns, seen from a distance. Name them:

1

2

3

Now this is a bit harder. Get your best specs out.

4 Name the hamlet.

5 Name the hamlet.

6 Name the hamlet.

Bowness and Windermere

7 What's the population of Bowness and Windermere, counting them as one town?

8 What was the original name of the village which is now Windermere?

9 When did the railway come to Windermere — and who tried to stop it?

10 After whom is St. Martin's Church, Bowness, supposedly named?

11 Belsfield is now a hotel. Which industrialist used to live there?

12 Which Queen has a Windermere hill named after her?

13 Name a pretty island near Bowness.

14 From which Head do you get a brill view of Windermere?

Keswick

15 What's the population of Keswick?

16 What's the Lake called at Keswick?

17 Name the oldest building in Keswick?

18 What's the river called which runs through Keswick?

19 Where will you see a one handed clock in Keswick?

20 What can you see at the Century in Keswick?

21 Which two famous poets lived in a building which is now part of Keswick School?

22 What's the local Keswick newspaper called?

Ambleside

23 What's the population of Ambleside?

24 What river flows through Ambleside?

25 Where in Ambleside do you get the Windermere boats?

26 Name the big college in Ambleside

27 Whose Garden Centre is in Ambleside?

28 What was the Roman Fort called that was just outside Ambleside?

29 Name the well-known waterfall outside Ambleside.

Cumbrian Towns

30 Carlisle has recently got itself a very smart, prize-winning shopping centre. What's it called?

31 Which TV company is based in Carlisle?

32 What's inside Tullie House, Carlisle?

33 Who and his sister went to school in Penrith?

34 Name the Parish Church of Penrith.

35 Cockermouth has got two rivers. Name them.

36 What's the main street in Cockermouth called?

37 What happens these days at the Brewery in Kendal?

38 What famous shoes are made in Kendal?

Main Streets

Some vintage photographs of the main streets in three Cumbrian towns — none of which is in the National Park.

39 Name the town, and the street.

40 Name the town, and the street.

41 Name the town, and the street.

Market Places

And now the Market Places and the Old Town Halls in three Cumbrian towns — only one of which is in the National Park.

42 Name the town.

43 Name the town.

44 Name the town.

45 In which Cumbrian town is Anne Tyson's cottage?

46 In which Cumbrian village is Sally Birkett's ale remembered?

47 In which hamlet did Judith Paris live?

48 A village and then a hamlet, each beginning with the letter S:

a

b

49 A Cumbrian town, and a large village, each beginning with the letter A

a

b

50 Let's finish at the seaside
a Costa del Solway. Where?
b Yummy seaside town in South Cumbria.

a

b

Section Four

Lakes

Rubbish – this isn't Thirlmere, we're in Ullswater...

Strangers might think that one bit of Cumbrian water looks like the next bit of Cumbrian water, but we Lakes Lovers can tell the difference. Well, sometimes we can. Other times it can be a bit hard, if you can only see a slice of a lake, or even just one bay, then you have to look for other evidence, such as the caption on the photograph. That's cheating. No captions in this chapter, but when a lake is illustrated, I've tried to play fair and give you a good chunk.

There are sixteen lakes in the Lake District, so most experts agree. ("The Good Guide to the Lakes" lists sixteen, and decrees all the others are tarns, so it must be true.)

In order of size they are:
Windermere,
Ullswater,
Coniston Water,
Bassenthwaite,
Haweswater,
Thirlmere,
Derwent Water,
Wast Water,
Crummock Water,
Ennerdale Water,
Esthwaite Water,
Buttermere,
Loweswater,
Grasmere,
Rydal Water,
Elterwater.

Now, look carefully at the titchy photographs of the sixteen lakes on the next two pages, numbered 1-16, and fit the right names to the right lake.

1

2

3

4

5

6

7

8

9

10

11

12

13

14

15

16

17 Windermere is the biggest, in fact the biggest in all England. How long is it?

18 Who was Windermere named after?

19 The Windermere Steamer Service sails between three piers — name them.

20 At one end of Windermere, there's a little railway. What's it called?

21 How does the Bowness Ferry get itself across the Lake:
a It's a hovercraft: b By steam engine: c It pulls itself across on a chain.

22 Name the castle on the eastern shore of Windermere.

23 Ullswater has three lake piers, used by the steamer service. Name them.

24 Who was Ullswater named after?

25 Wordsworth saw his daffodils on the shores of Ullswater. Where?

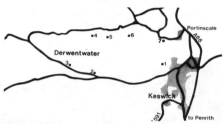

26 Derwent Water's launch service uses smaller boats than either Windermere or Ullswater — but they have more piers, seven in all. Can you name them?

27 Name Derwent Water's four islands.

28 Who was the famous author who lived on Derwent Water in a house called Brackenburn?

29 All the sixteen lakes except one have no need for the word 'lake' after their name, because they already end in either the word water or mere. So which is the only lake that needs the word lake?

30 Which is the deepest Lake?

31 Arrange in order of length — Grasmere, Esthwaite Water, Rydal, Haweswater.

32 On which Lake is Peel Island?

33 On which Lake does the Floating Island appear, usually seen only once every three years?

34 Which lake in the Lakes does Manchester get most of its water from?

35 Which is the only Lake, of the sixteen, which has no roads along any of its shores?

36 What Lake comes between Buttermere and Loweswater?

37 What Lake is named after swans?

Name the Lake View

38 Windermere, as you guessed at once. But which hotel lawns are these lovely people sitting on?

39 Buttermere: from which pass is the view?

40 Rydal Water: name the chunk of rock.

41 Derwent Water: name the hotel.

42 Derwent Water: name the crag.

43 Grasmere: from which bank?

44 Ullswater: from which Fell?

Name the Piers

45 Windermere: which promenade?

46 Derwent Water: which landing stage?

47 Grasmere: which hotel?

48 Windermere: which landing stage?

Boats

49 Some lovely old sailing boats — on which lake?

a

b

a Once seen on Coniston:

b Once seen on Ullswater:

c Still seen on Coniston.

Section Five

Mountains and Natural Features

Several Cumbrian newspapers, such as the Cumberland News, have a weekly photo competition to guess the mountain. I stare at them each week, but they all look the same, even when I've been up them umpteen times. It must be my eyes, or the rotten newsprint. When they give the answers the following week, I still rarely recognize them. So in this section, when I show you some rather indistinct photos of mountains, fells, passes, waterfalls and other natural features, I will give lots of clues. Honest.

Mountains

1 I don't believe metres will ever catch on, so name four Cumbrian peaks over 3,000 feet.

2 Which is the highest in Lakeland — and how big is it?

3 You must have climbed this summit. The lake in the background is Ullswater.

37

4 The summit of another Big One, with a lower slope to help you up.

5 Another hairy bit from a famous mountain. I'm sure you've stridden along it. See, I'm terribly helpful today.

6 That's me, well it could be, standing beside Sprinkling Tarn. What am I looking at?

7 We're at Wast Water this time. What's that nicely shaped mountain at the end?

8 Come on, look at that easy, grassy path. You can make it up — to which top?

9 We're in the Langdales, desperate for some refreshment. Heh, isn't that a hotel in the distance? What's it called?

10 Another very popular dale, the rival to Langdale.

11 Who climbed Scafell in 1802 and took his pen and ink with him to write a letter?

12 On what mountain is there a ravine called Piers Gill?

13 Jenkin Hill is a first slope on which mountain?

14 What's the Big Mountain near Red Tarn?

15 Where's Sharp Edge?

16 On which mountain is Nape's Needle?

17 What's the other name for Saddleback?

18 Dow Crag is the dodgy bit on which mountain?

19 Which lake does Catbells overlook?

20 Which is the fell Wainwright says he wants his ashes scattered on?

Passes

I find all passes hell to get up, and even heller to remember which was which afterwards. The following are five of the best known Passes: Honister, Whinlatter, Kirkstone, Newlands, Wrynose. That should make it easy. Just recognize some, then guess the rest.

21 Which pass? The clue is the Three Shires stone on top.

22 You've just motored over from Ambleside, so you must know where you are.

23 The road was pretty bad in those days, but the Pass could be done, for passengers between Borrowdale and Buttermere.

24 Don't worry. This is the quickest way from Keswick to Buttermere.

25 A rather easy pass, as passes go, for those wishing to roll down to Keswick from High Lorton.

Waterfalls

Now these really are hard. Once you've seen one waterfall view, you've seen them all. But these are very pretty shots of the four best known — Aira Force, Scale Force, Lodore Falls and Stock Ghyll Force — and I'll give you a few hints.

26 Lakeland's longest waterfall — 172 feet long.

27 Perhaps the most popular waterfall. Note the bridge.

28 Robert Southey, Poet Laureate, wrote a poem about these falls.

29 Not a huge waterfall, just 70 feet, but well loved by Ambleside folks.

30 Not a Pass, more a walk, if you can raise the energy . . .

31 Are Forestry Commission forests Natural Features? Hmm. Let's not get into arguments. Just name three of the four main Forestry Commission plantations in Lakeland.

32 This is definitely a natural feature — or did it fall off the back of a large lorry in Borrowdale? Been there for yonkers anyway. Name?

Place Names

A lot of Cumbrian place names come from the Norse, but have been altered slightly over the years. Here are literal translations of what some well known places originally meant. Can you guess their modern names?

33 Ulf's farm stead.

34 The clearing with the thorn bushes.

35 The cheese farm.

36 The dark blue or dark tarn.

37 Valley where rye is grown.

38 Water of the swans.

46

Rivers

39 On what river is Carlisle?

40 What river flows under Birks Bridge?

41 After which river did Coleridge name his son?

42 Out of which lake does the River Crake run?

Tarns

43 An islolated tarn, as big as a small lake.

44 Pretty tarn with Langdales behind.

45 Very pretty tarn, but how real is it?

46 That's Helvellyn behind: what's the tarn?

47 Feminists would probably want the name changed.

48 Nice look at the Scafell pikes: name the tarn.

49 Judith Paris was here.
50 Name the tarn with no name.

48

Section Six

Museums, Buildings

There are a surprising number of buildings open to the public in Cumbria, surprising if you're the sort of visitor who expects Lakeland to be all fells and sheep. There are Stately homes just as stately as any southern ones, as well as handsome castles, historic houses, fine churches, and excellent museums. We'll leave the Literary Places for the next chapter. . .

Stately Homes

There are three main ones — Holker Hall, Levens Hall and Dalemain. Which is which?

1 The best known Stately home in the Northern Lakes.

2 Hard to pronounce, but always lots going on.

3 Famous for its gardens.

49

Stately Castles

Two of these castles can be visited, and a good day out is guaranteed for all, but one is just a shell. All three are connected with famous Cumbrian families, two of them belted Earls. Name the castle — and the nob concerned.

4 An empty castle, but named after one of Cumbria's ruling families.

5 Recently opened to the public, so you might actually catch sight of the Earl inside.

6 Set in a Forest. Look out for the trees.

Stately Houses

7 A nicely rounded house — where is it?

8 Once a private home. Now Cumbria's most visited building.

9 Another castle, one connected in many people's minds with a railway.

10 Not a stately home, though the owners are trying terribly hard to bring in the visitors ...

Museums

11 Name two museums which specialise in Dolls. All right then, the names of the towns would do.

12 What does Jack Hadwin specialise in?

13 Where does the Border Regiment display itself?

14 Kendal has several museums, but name the fine building in the middle of the town which houses the town's best known museum.

15 Keswick has its museum beside which park?

16 While in Keswick, don't miss the seven foot pencil. Where?

17 Which museum has some good stuff on Fletcher Christian?

18 Where's the world's best Laurel & Hardy Museum?

19 Where can you see the shroud from St. Bees Man?

20 This is only a replica of Bluebird. Where can you see it?

21 Levens Hall has a good steam collection, but there's another Cumbrian place which specialises completely in steam stuff, such as this traction engine. Where?

22 As for steam boats, where can you see this 1911 Steam launch, Swallow?

23 Which stately home is the McCosh family associated with?

24 Which Cumbrian stately home does the Cavendish family live in?

25 What about the Bagots? Don't bother trying to pronounce it. Just name their pile.

26 Where the Strickland family lived for 700 years.

27 The National Trust's fine house in Troutbeck, once lived in by modest statesmen. Name it.

28 What are the main attractions of Acorn Bank and Lingholm?

29 If you keep walking through Nunnery Walk, what river do you come to?

30 Only two of these castles are intact — the rest are ruins. Name the two: Penrith Castle, Kendal Castle, Carlisle Castle, Appleby Castle, Egremont Castle.

31 Cumbria has only one cathedral. Where?

32 Perhaps the most visited Parish Church, thanks to the bodies.

33 Another Church with a famous grave. That's Skiddaw behind.

34 One of the small churches, but handy for a big climb after Helvellyn, or a swim across Thirlmere.

Stones

35 Ancient Stone Circle, not far from Keswick. Name?

36 Giant's Stones,
in Penrith. Where?

37 Emperor's Stones. Whose?

38 Where would you come across this charming little person?

ENGLAND'S GREATEST HISTORICAL SCENIC ROUTE

39 Billed as England's greatest scenic route. Where?

Name the Railway Stations

40 Definitely Inner City — still going strong.

41 No longer in use, but something exciting might happen soon to the site.

42 Gone, gone forever — what a shame . . .

Dead Villages

Now museum pieces, if you can find them, should the weather be terribly dry.

43 The lake is still there, but the fishermen's inn has gone.

44 The Dun Bull Inn. Where was it?

45 A church, now drowned. Where?

Bridges

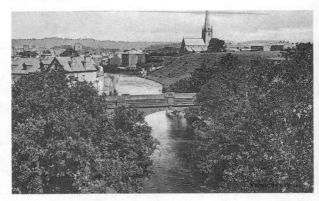

46 Name the bridge and the town.

47 Now owned by National Trust. Where?

48 Step carefully. Where?

49 Watch out for the photographers. Where?

50 Name the building: terribly isolated, right at the back of a famous mountain. In 1987, it becomes a YHA.

Section Seven

Literary

Can any other little rural area in the whole of Britain, perhaps even the world, have so many literary associations? Lakeland does seem to have more than its fair share. Not just Willy Wordsworth, but a whole host of golden writers have lived in the Lakes at some time.

Literary Homes

We start with six homes, all open to the public, each connected with well-known writers. Name the house — and the writer. Three of them were lived in by W. Wordsworth, so that makes it easy.

1 Nice views, overlooking Coniston, though the literary resident did go a bit potty towards the end.

2 Rather imposing for a man by then of some importance.

3 Not a famous writer's home, but a place visited by many scribes, on the shores of Bass Lake. Very inspirational.

4 V. small res., but what a lot they crammed in.

5 Pretty farmhouse. Well known for its animals.

6 Georgian gem, would suit someone perhaps working for a local lordling.

Now some harder homes. Famous writers did live in them in the past, but they are not open to visitors today.

7 Two brothers in law lived here, both poets. Now part of a school.

8 Des. res, good views of Derwentwater, suit author writing chronicles.

9 Now a little guest house, but young Hartley Coleridge once lived here, and so did Thos de Quincey.

10 The house below was called Dove Nest and the lady who once lived there wrote "The Boy Stood on the Burning Deck". Bet you can't name her.

Wordsworth

11 Where was he born — and in what year?

12 What was his father's profession?

13 We know he had a sister, Dorothy — did he have any brothers? If so, how many?

14 As a boy, he lived for a while in Penrith and used to climb this hill outside the town, later written about in the Prelude. Name the Hill.

15 He went to this Grammar School. Where?

16 He then went on to Oxbridge. Which college?

17 I hardly dare talk about this, and it was hushed up in his lifetime, but he had this, well, affair in France with this girl who got, eh, pregnant. Name the girl, and Wordsworth's illegitimate daughter.

a   b

18 Two other women played a big part in his life — his wife Mary and his daughter Dora. Which is which?

19 In all, he lived in three houses in Grasmere. Here's one. Name them all.

20 He managed to procure himself a job in the end, not as a poet or writer. What as?

21 Here's four lines of Wordsworth, each from a different poem — and one line I have made up. Identify the source of each line.

Oft have I heard of Lucy Gray

A poet could not but be gay

For from her face I oft did hide

Tis three feet long and two feet wide.

Lake Poets

a   b

22 Two fine young poets, with lovely neckerchiefs, who married sisters called Fricker. Name them.

23 Which local newspaper did Thomas de Quincey become editor of?

24 Which poet wrote a history of Brazil, without actually ever going to Brazil?

25 Who wrote "Confessions of an English Opium-Eater"?

Ruskin

a   b

26 These two monuments, each in a different place, commemorate John Ruskin. Where are they?

27 What line of business was Ruskin's father in? (They sell examples of his produce at Brantwood today.)

28 Which famous English artist is Ruskin best known for encouraging? (He also did some Lakeland scenes.)

Beatrix Potter

29 Where did Beatrix Potter's father get his family money from?

30 Which Lakeland cleric encouraged her to be a writer?

31 Her first book was published in 1901. Name it.

32 She stopped writing after she married a local chap, Mr. William Heelis. What did he do for a living?

33 What were Beatrix Potter's favourite sheep?

34 Which body did she leave most of her property and possessions to?

Arthur Ransome

Ransome had boyhood holidays in the Lakes, and later lived in the Coniston and Windermere area, using it as a setting for his "Swallows and Amazons" books which first appeared in 1930. But he didn't always keep the original place names. Can you cope? (You have to be a Ransome expert to even understand the questions. If not, I'd give up at once and go on to the next chapter . . .).

35 Where was Wild Cat Island?

36 Which Lakeland mountain did he call Kanchenjunga?

37 Where is Octopus lagoon?

38 Which Lakeland town is Rio?

39 What does Capt. Flint's houseboat do today.

General Lit

40 Where did Tennyson have his honeymoon?

41 Charles Dickens and Wilkie Collins had a holiday together in Cumbria in 1857. Name two villages they stayed at.

42 What publication emerged, based on the Cumbrian adventures of Dickens and Wilkie Collins?

43 "Christopher North" was a writer, wrestler, friend of Wordsworth. What was his real name?

44 Which writer visited Southey in Keswick but had to leave in a hurry, after he'd become too friendly with a local girl?

45 Who described the Castlerigg stones as a "dismal cirque"?

46 Which Scottish writer, friend of the Wordsworths, got married in Carlisle Cathedral?

Autographs

Four nice literary autographs for your collection. Name the signature and the face. Gosh, this is an easy one . . .

Wm Wordsworth

47

a

Thomas de Quincey

48

b

W Ruskin

49

c

Beatrix Potter

50

d

Section Eight

People

Lots of other well-known folks have lived in or been associated with the Lakes, apart from all those Literary Types. In fact, every civilised Britisher expects to visit the Lakes, at least once in a lifetime. Here's some questions on those who have gone before, or are there today ...

Lords and Nobs

1 We'll start with the poshos. The leading Lord in Cumbria is the Earl of Lonsdale. What's his family name?

2 Whose father was employed by the family in the 1770's?

3 The fifth Earl of Lonsdale, who died in 1947, was a bit eccentric, known as the Yellow Earl. What connection does he have with the Automobile Association — then and now?

4 What did the Yellow Earl do for Boxing?

5 The other notable Cumbrian toff is the Earl of Carlisle. Here's a monument to the family in Brampton. What's the family name?

6 Name the more recently ennobled Lord, stalwart of the Tory Party, who has the same initials as an ex Poet Laureate.

7 Still with the same initials, gee what a coincidence, who was the anti-slavery campaigner who stayed in the Lakes in the early 1800's?

8 One of Henry VIII's wives, born in Kendal in 1512.

9 Which Queen had an enforced visit to Carlisle Castle in 1568?

10 Which Princeling captured Carlisle in 1745?

11 Famous headmaster who retired to Ambleside in 1834.

12 Keswick Canon, one of the founders of the National Trust.

13 Famous Judge, born in Ulverston 1883, campaigner against Ullswater becoming a reservoir.

14 Famous comedian, also born in Ulverston, 1890.

15 Which Quaker lived for a time in Ulverston and married a local girl?

16 Amazing to think that three famous people were born around Cockermouth, all within a few years of each other: a Mutineer, born 1764: b Atom theorist, born 1766: c Poet, born 1770

17 Name the huntsman.

18 Where was he born and buried?

19 Name the modern poet, born in Millom, 1914.

20 Yummy looking broadcaster, novelist, man of the arts, from Wigton, born 1939.

21 Mountaineer, based in Caldbeck since 1974.

22 Who was the flashman born in Carlisle in 1925?

23 Racing driver, killed Coniston, 1967.

24 Formerly the wife of a Fab Four, now living in Penrith.

The Blessed Wainwright

25 Where was A. Wainwright born?

26 What does the 'A' stand for?

27 How many books made up his "Pictorial Guide to the Lakeland Fells"?

28 Who publishes his Guides?

29 Before becoming a writer, what job did he have in Cumbria, and where?

30 What a lovely photograph. How did he get them to stand in those positions? It's Keswick of course, as you knew, but who's the photographer?

31 Pretty portrait. Done by a famous artist, died in Kendal.

Right, you know these Cumbrians well, so to save space I'm only showing part of their anatomy.

32 Whose boots?

33 Whose hand?

34 Whose hat?

35 Whose hair?

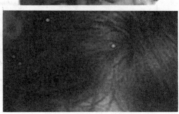

36 What did Haskett Smith do in 1886 that so amazed all climbing folk?

37 Mary of Buttermere lived in, wait for it, Buttermere. But where?

38 A blackguard calling himself "The Hon. Col. Hope" came along in 1802 and did something dastardly to her. What?

39 What happened to him?

40 Where is Mary buried?

41 John Paul Jones, founder of the USA Navy, took it upon himself in 1778 to raid which Cumbrian harbour?

42 John Parker has written many walking guides to Lakeland. What's his real name?

Who Wrote the Letters?

Three greats from the past

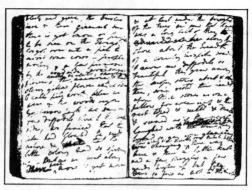

43

45

Five modern day letters. The addresses should help.

46

Dev HUNT (↶)
Jar in for 30ᵗʰ. God idea
J & x
MELV (YN)

London Weekend Television,
Kent House, Upper Ground, London SE1 9LT. Telephone: 01-261 3434

47

HOUSE OF LORDS
LONDON SW1A 0PW

6th April, 1984

Dear Mr. Davies,

Thank you so much for sending me a copy
of your Lakeland book. It was very good of
you and I shall certainly enjoy it very much.

Yours sincerely,

48

ROSE CASTLE
DALSTON
CARLISLE
CA5 7BZ   27th March 1984

Dear Hunter,

Thank you so much for the advanced copy of the book. It
will now go into the Archives at Rose but not in the section
which is never looked at but the one where books are continually
borrowed.

Warm good wishes,
Yours sincerely,

49

ESTATE OFFICE,
LOWTHER,
PENRITH,
CUMBRIA,
CA10 2HG

23rd March 1984

Dear Mʳ Hunter Davies,

How very kind of you to send me a pre-publication copy of your first venture
as a publisher. I think the "Good Guide to the Lakes" is very interesting
and a new and chatty approach. I am horrified you put so much about us in
and no doubt we shall have even more people banging on our door at Askham
Hall, despite the sign at the entrance saying 'Private', as a result of your
comments in your little piece on Askham as "a recommended village"!

Yours sincerely,
J Ross Lonsdale

50

KENDAL

Dear Mr Davies.
          It's a pleasure
          But why a London address
when Lakeland is at its enchanting
best?
                    Sincerely
                    a wainwright

Section Nine

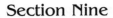

Sports, Entertainments and Customs

They have some funny customs, those Cumbrian folks. Make sure you catch them at it. And make sure you find out exactly what's going on. Then you'll be able to answer all these funny questions ...

1 What sport and where?

2 There are six main fox hunting packs in Cumbria — name three of them.

3 Which sports normally take place on the third Thursday after the first Monday in August?

4 Early in June each year, usually the second Wednesday, there's a big do in Appleby. What's the main attraction?

5 Rushbearing was the old custom of strewing church floors with rushes. Still takes place in several villages in Cumbria each year. Name three.

6 At the Egremont Crab Fair, do you:
a Pick crab apples: b Eat shell fish: c Watch Cumbrian sports.

7 A "gurning" competition is one of the traditional Cumbrian events at Egremont Crab Fair. What is being judged?

8 What annual Cumbrian competition is Will Ritson credited with beginning?

9 In what sport has Joss Naylor been a champion?

10 What sport remembers Joe Bowman?

11 Is the Fairfield Horseshoe:
a Something thrown in a traditional Cumbrian sport?
b A prize for Cumberland and Westmorland Wrestlers?
c A string of fells you walk up and down?

12 Who's George Bowman and at what sports event in Cumbria has he beaten Prince Philip?

13 Has Carlisle United ever been in the First Division? If so, when?

14 Name Carlisle United's ground.

15 What's the most obvious difference between Cumbrian fox hunting and fox hunting elsewhere?

16 Did John Peel have 'a coat so gay' or 'a coat so grey'?

17 In hound trailing, what scent are the hounds following?

18 What breed of ancient fish, a bit like a trout, might you catch in Windermere?

19 According to legend, Herdwick sheep, Lakeland's native breed, came originally from which country, 400 years ago?

20 And according to folk lore, how do Herdwicks keep themselves alive when they have no food?

21 What's dry about dry stone walls?

22 What's unusual about a Cumbrian fell pony?

23 If you heard a Cumbrian shepherd saying "yan, tan, tether", what would he be doing?

24 What does a Cumbrian farmer mean when he talks about: a A hogg: b A tup: c A gimmer.

25 Cumbrian names are heavily Norse. What do these mean in normal English:
a Thwaite: b Force: c Holm: d How: e Ghyll: f Hause: g Nab: h Pike: i Skarth.

26 What's the name of Keswick's Theatre?

27 In which Forest is The Theatre in the Forest?

28 In which town is the Royalty Cinema?

Shops

Don't say you didn't go in any. I saw you. And it wasn't just for Kendal Mint Cake. So what do the following firms and people specialise in?

29 Romneys, Kendal.

30 Dalesman, Clapham.

31 Peter Bland, Kendal.

32 Booths, Bowness.

33 George Fisher, Keswick.

34 Fred Holdsworth, Ambleside.

35 Michael Moon, Whitehaven.

36 Walter Willson, Keswick.

37 Heaton Cooper, Grasmere.

38 Frank Peters, Kendal.

39 Tiffen King Nicholson.

40 Lovely Symbol, Lovely Lettering — but what do these two companies specialise in?

RIBBLE

41 The Ribble is a river. In Cumbria it also means what?

42 The mountain goat is an animal. In Cumbria it also means what?

Native Names

Someone who comes from London is called a Londoner. What's a person from these places called?

43 Barrow.

44 Keswick.

45 Grasmere.

46 Cockermouth.

47 Kendal.

48 Westmorland.

49 Carlisle.

50 Penrith.

Section Ten

Fun and Games

Rather more light hearted this section. Well, your tired old brain has been rather taxed so far. Sorry about that. So just relax. Some easy things to do, for children of all ages. And some amusements.

1 Who is this fine looking figure of a man?
a Melvyn Bragg before going into make-up at LWT.
b Westmorland shepherd, 1920.
c Chris Bonington, after Everest.

2 What are these seven likely lads doing?
a The chorus line from a touring company of Privates on Parade.
b Modelling the latest underwear for Marks & Spencer, Carlisle.
c Cumberland and Westmorland Wrestlers, about to throw each other.

3 Where in Cumbria do you regularly see this illustration?
a On the Earl of Lonsdale's notepaper.
b On the front page of the Whitehaven News.
c In advertisements for Sellafield.

True or False

4 Dorothy's Journal is:—

a A weekly newspaper in Grasmere.

b A feminist book manifesto.

c Dorothy Wordsworth's notebook.

5 Arthur's Pike is:—

a Famous fish caught by Mr. Scargill.

b Big fell overlooking Ullswater.

c Relic of King Arthur on show at Holker Hall.

6 Dollywagon is:—

a The taking home of a drunken washerwoman as described in Wordsworth's 'The Prelude'.

b The last train on the Carlisle Silloth Railway.

c A peak in the Hellvellyn range.

7 Which of these are not Cumbrian mountains or fells:—

a High Raise

b High Stile

c High Hopes

d High Gang

e High Street

f High There

8 Ulpha is:—

a A letter in the Greek alphabet:

b Norse for half (as in 'ulpha pint'):

c A hamlet in Dunnerdale:

d A dun in Hammerdale.

9 Which of these is not in Great Langdale:—

a Stickle Gill:

b Pike O'Stickle:

c Stickle Pickle:

d Pike O'Blisco.

10 Stool End is:—

a A farm in Langdale:

b A school in Hawkshead:

c A lavatory in Windermere.

11 Jack's Rake is:—

a Part of Pavey Ark:

b Part of Noah's Ark:

c What Peter Rabbit stood on in Mr. McGregor's garden.

Awful Names

12 A northern fell which sounds a terrible mistake.

13 What you might do when enquiring which village Lord Lonsdale lived in.

14 Where to bathe in a cold stream.

15 This village must be on the foot of Eskdale.

16 If you were walking round Derwentwater and heard some feline sounds, where might they be coming from?

17 What crags need ironing?

18 What crag should be in a monastery?

19 What mountain sounds like the end of a house?

20 Which pass should Boy Scouts be able to untie?

21 Which mountain sounds like something from John le Carré?

22 Why is southern Lakeland so hot?

23 What did the Red Indian say to the village on Ullswater?

24 What village in the northern fells sounds cross?

25 What should really be the shallowest lake?

26 Who's the geriatric sitting above Coniston?

27 At which tarn should pigs gather?

28 In which dale should pigs gather?

29 Which waterfall would the RAF like to fly over?

30 You have to be lucky to live in this place on Morecambe Bay.

Unscramble these place names

31 Kwik Sec.

32 Walt Urles.

33 Slic Earl.

34 Snob Sew.

35 Bum Reetter.

Hidden Words

In five minutes, make twenty words, of at least two letters each, out of:—

36 WINDERMERE.

37 COCKERMOUTH.

38 WORDSWORTH.

39 AMBLESIDE.

40 CUMBERLAND.

41 WESTMORLAND.

Odd Maps

Because of the rotten weather, ruining the stuff in your rucksack, your maps have come to pieces. Which towns are these part of?

42

43

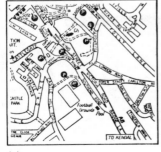

44

45

Pronunciations

46 How do you say the "Burgh" in Burgh-by-Sands:—

a Burg: b Bruff: c Boro.

47 How do you say "Broughton" in Broughton-in-Furness:—

a Bruffen: b Brutten: c Brought'n.

48 Should Sedbergh be said:—

a Sedber: b Sedboro: c Sedbruff.

49 Brougham Castle near Penrith should be:—

a Broom: b Brum: c Bruffam.

50 Robert Southey, the Poet Laureate, should be said:—

a Sootey: b South - y: c Suth - y.

Puzzling Places

51 In the left hand column are the first syllables of well-known Cumbrian places. But they don't go with the right hand column. Can you find the correct ending from the right hand column to go with a word from the left hand, to form a real place name.

Al	row
Amble	rock
Arm	ham
Bar	foot
Beck	both
Borrow	pot
Butter	side
Car	port
Dale	dale
Dear	cock
Kirk	scale
Load	stone
Mary	mere
Saddle	end
Sea	haven
Town	nose
White	main
Wry	back

Ancient Ads . . .

These two advertisements appeared in an 1881 guide book to the Lakes. Study them carefully for half a minute, then cover each of them up, because I'm going to ask a few questions . . .

QUEEN'S HOTEL,
KESWICK.

UNDER VERY DISTINGUISHED PATRONAGE.

THE above Hotel has been refurnished throughout in the most modern style, and no expense spared to add to the comfort of visitors. The Coffee Room is the most spacious in the town; the Sitting and Bed Rooms are large and well aired, and the views from the windows of the lake and mountain scenery are unequalled. Every endeavour has been used to make the sanitary arrangements perfect.

COACHES AND CONVEYANCES TO EVERY PLACE OF INTEREST IN THE LAKE DISTRICT.

MOUNTAIN PONIES, GUIDES, BOATS, AND BOATMEN.

HOT AND COLD BATHS. BILLIARDS.

PARTIES BOARDED BY WEEK OR MONTH.

CHARGES STRICTLY MODERATE.

WINES AND SPIRITS OF THE BEST QUALITY.

GEORGE STAMPER, Proprietor.

52 What's the name of the Keswick hotel?
Which room is the most spacious in town?
Which rooms are well aired?
Inside the hotel, what facilities do they boast about?
Outside, what services can they offer?
Who's the proprietor?

Postal Telegraph Office and Pillar Letter-Box are placed in the Hotel.

CLOUDSDALE'S CROWN HOTEL,

WINDERMERE

(Patronized by Royalty and American Presidents),

IS ONE OF THE MOST COMFORTABLE AND BEST MANAGED HOTELS IN THE LAKE COUNTRY. Situate in its own grounds, above the village of Bowness. It maintains its pre-eminence as the principal Hotel in the place, and the general remark is, " Here you find an air of refinement different to the surroundings of the other Hotels," all situated in the lower part of the village. The Hotel makes up Ninety Beds, and has a proportionate number of Sitting Rooms. An elegant Coffee and Ladies' Drawing Room; also a Billiard Room. **District Coaches run from the " Crown "** for Ambleside, Grasmere, and Keswick; also for Coniston and Ullswater during the Season. The WINDERMERE STEAM YACHTS ply several times daily from the Pier in front of the Hotel, up the Lake to Ambleside and down the Lake to Newby Bridge Lake Side Railway Station. Omnibuses and Servants attend the arrival of each Train at Windermere Station, to convey parties to the Crown Hotel and Bowness; distance 1¼ mile.

TABLE D'HOTE, DAILY, AT 6.30 P.M.; SUNDAYS AT 3 P.M.

FAMILIES BOARDED BY THE WEEK OR MONTH.

*** The pre-eminence of the " CROWN " is indicated by the fact that the Hotel has been made a Postal-Telegraph Station by Government Authority.

53 What's the name of the Windermere hotel?
Who has patronized it?
How many beds are there?
Where do District coaches run to?
Where do the Windermere Steam yachts ply?
How far is the hotel from Windermere Station?
What time on Sunday is the table D'Hote?
What modern invention indicates its 'pre-eminence'?

ACROSS

1 — The place Old Tilli cleared near Wetherlam. (13)

9 — Walpole sent one such to Watendlath. (5)

10 — In French direction to way with drink on the Western side. (9)

12 — Fell near Buttermere, with Her Majesty's ships leading. (9)

13 — Loud organ without an Eastern ending will make a false impression. (5)

14 — Boat log could hold equipment. (4-3)

16 — Ship combined with Royal Mail Service to produce crustaceans. (7)

18 — Gloomy ravine near Harter Fell, but learner is potentially glad. (7)

20 — Zinc pole supporting Rothay crossing (7)

22 — Student rating the Spanish for identification. (5)

24 — Valley enclosure could make Earth glad. (9)

26 — Artists and don may loiter and get confused on the mountain. (9)

27 — Enough to make drunken teal on the Eastern side chipper. (5)

28 — Throw Bert's ear towards Kirkstone . . . has had its tragedy. (13)

DOWN

2 — Broken leg embedded in timber. Not surprising with all those trees. (9)

3 — The start of a popular pond and the sound of Lakeland's hardiest inhabitants. (5)

4 - A distillation of free gin, but tacking's more often needed on Windermere. (7)

5 — Shrugs at Germans surrounding dead guerrilla. They had feelings it might happen. (7)

6 — The boys in blue as our Italian friend might put it at the Ullswater spectacular. (4,5)

7 — The short academic has sex appeal, but would prefer the money! (6)

8 — The student has no more than a 50-50 chance of getting to one of its concerts. (6)

11 — There's plenty of this around here, but the higher the rarer. (3)

15 — I am jammed between fish and insect. Fab is, I believe, still the word for it. (9)

17 — It sounds like the valley where the bishop lives. Item is ruined on the way to a drink. (9)

18 — In France is he wise to store fodder? (6)

19 — Lord's entrance in London? (7)

20 — Greetings given by mornings, alas, in reverse. (7)

21 — A bit of cobbling concerning a cad. (6)

23 — See 3. This is the way it is . . . and the same to you. (3)

25 — It could be a great Cumbrian river. (5)

Cumbrian Dialect

55 Deear me, hoo t' times hes alter't sen Ah went ta
scheul. T' oald things hes varrily geen pleàce till t' new,
an', wheddr for t' better or t' warse, Ah cannet tell;
mebbe sum things better, an' sum warse.

Ah was just thinkin' t' udder neet hoo' t' kustoms hes
chang't in ooar oan villidge. Reely yan cannet imagin'
it's t' seàm pleàce; an' Ah just menshun't it till ooar
Jim, bit he nobbet sed, "Nivver mind t' villidge — let's
off ta bed."

Can you translate the above? Please don't cheat too
quickly, but here's a translation.

Dear me, how times have altered since I went to
school. The old things have really given place to the
new, and whether for better or worse, I can't say;
maybe some things are better, and some things
worse.

I was just thinking the other night how things have
changed in our own village. Really, one can't imagine
it's the same place; and I just mentioned it to our Jim,
but he only said, "Never mind the village, let's off to
bed."

Thanks to Colin Shelbourn of Windermere for the ten
new cartoons. To Arthur Jones of Windermere for the
Crossword. To Wendy Sturgess of BBC TV for the photie
on the inside of the rear cover. To Frederick Warne,
Publishers, for permission to reproduce the Beatrix
Potter on page 18 and to Abbot Hall Gallery, Kendal for
permission to reproduce the Romney on page 72. And
even more thanks to the photographers, mostly
unknown, who took the old picture postcards.

ANSWERS

Section One: General Information

1 1 Lake District
2 Northumberland
3 North York Moors
4 Yorkshire Dales
5 Peak District   6 Snowdonia
7 Brecon Beacons
8 Pembrokeshire Coast
9 Exmoor   10 Dartmoor

2 1 Brecon   2 Dartmoor
3 Exmoor   4 Lake District
5 North Yorks
6 Northumberland
7 Peak District
8 Pembrokeshire   9 Snowdonia
10 Yorkshire Dales

3 USA, Yellowstone Park, 1872
4 1951
5 880 sq. miles
6 Lake District Special Planning Board
7 Green jumpers with an oatmeal stripe across the front
8 Kendal, Cockermouth, Penrith
9 Kendal
10 a
11 Kirkstone
12 J36
13 None — the M6 does not enter the NP. Got you there.
14 J44
15 1 hr. — it's 60 miles approx.
16 A591
17 Still the A591
18 Ullswater
19 Windermere
20 Crummock
21 Hardknott, Wrynose
22 S — N
23 Grasmere
24 Penrith, Kendal
25 Oxenholme
26 Carnforth

27 Cockermouth, Keswick & Penrith Rly. Co. Easy, eh.
28 Newcastle & Carlisle; Maryport & Carlisle; Lancaster & Carlisle; Caledonian; Glasgow Dumfries & Carlisle (later the Glasgow & SW); Carlisle & Silloth Bay (later the North British Railway); Midland (Settle & Carlisle).
29 1 Carlisle   2 Allerdale
3 Eden   4 Copeland
5 S. Lakeland   6 Barrow
30 Carlisle
31 Appleby
32 a Carlisle   b Kendal
c Workington
33 NP
34 Brockhole, Windermere
35 N.Trust — 125,000 acres; Forestry Comm. — 32,000; NP — 19,000 acres
36 478,000
37 41,000
38 NW — 36%; NE — 17%; London & SE — 14%
39 Carlisle
40 Carlisle's Roman name
41 122 A.D.
42 Bowness on Solway
43 Stream
44 Cymry or Cymri
45 Small farmers
46 Local cloth
47 Burgh Marsh
48 a Weather forecast
b Cumbria Tourist Board
c NP Authority   d Cumbria County Council
49 a Keswick   b Kendal
c Grasmere   d Pooley Bridge
50 999 — then ask Police to call them

Section Two: **Hotels**

1 top, Howtown Hotel
bottom, Miller Howe
2 a Miller Howe b Howtown
3 750
4 Sharrow Bay
5 Miller Howe
6 Low Wood, Windermere —
130 bedrooms
7 a Bowness b Bowness
c Ambleside
8 Lodore Swiss Hotel —
Borrowdale, Keswick
9 Miller Howe branch — in
Cartmel
10 Royal Oak
11 Little Langdale
12 Keswick
13 Keswick Hotel; Old England,
Bowness
14 Castle Inn
15 Sharrow Bay
16 Miller Howe
17 Ambleside
18 Windermere
19 Bowness
20 Penrith
21 Ambleside
22 Grasmere
23 Grasmere
24 Keswick
25 Brantwood, Dove Cottage
26 Bowness

27 Bassenthwaite, Ireby,
Windermere, Kirkby Lonsdale,
Hawkshead, Crook, Newton
Reigny, Arlecdon, Barrow
28 Caldbeck
29 Jennings
30 Hartleys
31 Caffle House
32 Photographers
33 Bluebell
34 a Troutbeck b Flookburgh
35 a Staveley
b Crook
c Ravenstonedale
36 Grasmere Gingerbread
37 Quiggin, Romneys, Wilson,
Wiper
38 b
39 c
40 Disabled
41 a Ambleside
b Black Sail
c Grasmere — Butharlyp
d Patterdale
42 Scafell Hotel, Rosthwaite
43 Ullswater Hotel, Glenridding
44 Skinburness Hotel, Silloth
45 Kendal
46 Pubs in the Carlisle District,
1916-1971
47 Beatrix Potter
48 The Tale of Jemima
Puddleduck
49 Sawrey
50 The National Trust

Section Three: **Towns**

1 Keswick
2 Ambleside
3 Coniston
4 Watendlath
5 Howtown
6 Grange in Borrowdale
7 8,500
8 Birthwaite
9 1848 — Wordsworth
10 A Roman soldier
11 H. W. Schneider
12 Queen Adelaide
13 Belle Isle
14 Orrest Head
15 4,762
16 Derwent Water
17 Crosthwaite Church, 1181
18 R. Greta
19 Moot Hall
20 Plays
21 Coleridge & Southey
22 Keswick Reminder
23 2,671
24 R. Rothay
25 Waterhead

26 Charlotte Mason
27 Hayes
28 Galava
29 Stock Ghyll Force
30 The Lanes
31 Border TV
32 Museum
33 Wordsworth & Dorothy
34 St. Andrew's
35 R. Cocker, R. Derwent
36 Main St. Easy, huh.
37 Arts Centre
38 K Shoes
39 Cockermouth
40 Kendal
41 Wigton
42 Carlisle
43 Brampton
44 Keswick
45 Hawkshead
46 Troutbeck
47 Watendlath
48 a Sawrey b Seatoller
49 a Alston b Allonby
50 a Silloth b Barrow

Section Four: **Lakes**

1 Ullswater
2 Rydal
3 Bassenthwaite
4 Buttermere
5 Wastwater
6 Grasmere
7 Crummock
8 Haweswater
9 Windermere
10 Thirlmere
11 Esthwaite
12 Ennerdale
13 Coniston
14 Derwent Water
15 Loweswater
16 Elterwater
17 10 miles
18 Norse hero — Winand or Winande
19 1 Lakeside
2 Bowness 3 Waterhead
20 Lakeside — Haverthwaite Rlwy.
21 c
22 Wray Castle
23 1 Pooley Bridge
2 Howtown 3 Glenridding
24 Another Norse hero — L'Ulf
25 Gowbarrow Pk.
26 1 Keswick
2 Ashness Gate 3 Lodore
4 High Brandlehow
5 Low Brandlehow 6 Hawes End
7 Nichol End

27 Derwent, Lord's, Rampsholme, St. Herbert's
28 Sir Hugh Walpole
29 Bassenthwaite Lake
30 Wast Water — 258 feet deep
31 Haweswater, 4 mls; Esthwaite, 1½ mls; Grasmere, 1; Rydal ¾.
32 Coniston
33 Derwent Water
34 Thirlmere
35 Ennerdale Water
36 Crummock
37 Elterwater (Elter is old Norse for swan)
38 Old England Hotel
39 Honister
40 Poet's Seat
41 Lodore Swiss
42 Friar's Crag
43 Red Bank
44 Gowbarrow Fell
45 Bowness
46 Keswick
47 Prince of Wales
48 Waterhead
49 a Windermere
b Crummock
50 a Lady of the Lake
b Raven c Gondola

Section Five: **Mountains**

1 Scafell Pike; Scafell, Helvellyn, Skiddaw
2 Scafell Pike — 3210 feet
3 Helvellyn
4 Skiddaw
5 Striding Edge, Helvellyn
6 Great End
7 Great Gable
8 Skiddaw
9 Dungeon Ghyll Hotel
10 Borrowdale
11 S. T. Coleridge
12 Scafell Pike
13 Skiddaw
14 Helvellyn
15 Saddleback
16 Great Gable
17 Blencathra
18 Coniston Old Man
19 Derwent Water
20 Haystacks
21 Wrynose
22 Kirkstone
23 Honister
24 Newlands
25 Whinlatter

26 Scale Force
27 Aira Force
28 Lodore
29 Stock Ghyll
30 Dunmail Raise
31 Grizedale, Ennerdale, Thornthwaite, Dodd Wood
32 Bowder Stone
33 Ulverston
34 Thornthwaite
35 Keswick
36 Blea Tarn
37 Rydal
38 Elterwater, as you already know. Just checking.
39 Eden
40 Duddon
41 Derwent
42 Coniston
43 Devokewater
44 Blea Tarn
45 Tarn Hows
46 Red Tarn
47 Brotherswater
48 Styhead Tarn
49 Watendlath
50 Innominate

Section Six: **Museums**

1 Dalemain
2 Holker Hall
3 Levens Hall
4 Lowther Castle (Earl of Lonsdale)
5 Naworth (Earl of Carlisle)
6 Hutton in the Forest (Lord Inglewood)
7 Belle Isle
8 Brockhole — NP Centre
9 Muncaster
10 Sellafield
11 Dolls House Museum, Ambleside; Costume Dolls Gallery, Cockermouth
12 Motorcycles — at Broughton
13 Carlisle Castle
14 Abbot Hall
15 Fitz Park
16 Pencil Museum
17 Maryport Maritime Museum
18 Ulverston
19 Whitehaven Museum
20 Lakeland Motor Museum, Holker Hall
21 Penrith Steam Museum
22 Windermere Steamboat Museum
23 Dalemain
24 Holker Hall
25 Levens Hall
26 Sizergh Castle
27 Townend
28 Gardens
29 R. Eden
30 Carlisle, Appleby
31 Carlisle
32 Grasmere
33 Crosthwaite, Keswick
34 Wythburn Church
35 Castlerigg
36 St. Andrew's churchyard
37 Hadrian's Wall (Walltown Crag)
38 Roman statue — Tullie House, Carlisle
39 Settle — Carlisle Rlwy.
40 Carlisle
41 Keswick
42 Cockermouth
43 Anglers Inn, Ennerdale
44 Mardale, Haweswater
45 Mardale
46 Jubilee, Cockermouth
47 Old Bridge, Ambleside
48 Stepping Stones, Ambleside
49 Ashness, Derwent Water
50 Skiddaw House or Hut

Section Seven: **Literary**

1 Brantwood — John Ruskin
2 Rydal Mount — Wordsworth
3 Mirehouse
4 Dove Cottage — Wordsworth
5 Hill Top Farm — Beatrix Potter
6 Wordsworth House, Cockermouth
7 Greta Hall, Keswick School — Coleridge & Southey
8 Brackenburn — Sir Hugh Walpole
9 Nab Cottage
10 Felicia Hemons
11 Cockermouth — 1770
12 Lawyer — agent for the Lowthers
13 3 brothers — Richard, John, Christopher
14 Beacon
15 Hawkshead Grammar School
16 St. John's, Cambridge
17 Annette Vallon — daughter Caroline
18 a Mary b Dora
19 Allan Bank, plus Dove Cottage and the Parsonage
20 Distributor of stamps for Westmorland
21 Line 1 — Lucy Gray
Line 2 — Daffodils
Line 3 — made up
Line 4 — The Thorn
22 a Coleridge b Southey
23 Westmorland Gazette
24 Southey
25 De Quincey
26 a Coniston Churchyard
b Friar's Crag, Keswick
27 Wine importer, particularly sherry
28 Turner
29 Lancashire cotton
30 Canon Rawnsley
31 Peter Rabbit
32 Solicitor
33 Herdwick
34 National Trust
35 Peel Island, Coniston
36 Coniston Old Man
37 Allan Tarn, Coniston
38 Bowness on Windermere
39 The Gondola — sailing on Coniston
40 Mirehouse, Bass Lake, and Tent Lodge, Coniston
41 Hesket Newmarket, Allonby, Wigton
42 "The Lazy Tour of Two Idle Apprentices"
43 John Wilson
44 Wllm Hazlitt
45 John Keats
46 Sir Walter Scott
47 W. Wordsworth
48 Thomas De Quincey
49 J. Ruskin
50 Beatrix Potter

Section Eight: **People**

1. Lowther
2. Wordsworth's
3. 1st President of the AA; their colour is also yellow
4. Gave Lonsdale Belt
5. Howard
6. Lord (Willy) Whitelaw
7. William Wilberforce
8. Katherine Parr
9. Mary Queen of Scots
10. Bonny Prince Charlie
11. Dr. Thomas Arnold
12. Canon Rawnsley
13. Lord (Norman) Birkett
14. Stan Laurel
15. George Fox
16. a Fletcher Christian
    John Dalton
    William Wordsworth
17. John Peel
18. Caldbeck
19. Norman Nicholson
20. Melvyn Bragg
21. Chris Bonington
22. George McDonald Fraser
23. Donald Campbell
24. Cynthia Lennon
25. Blackburn
26. Alfred
27. 7
28. Westmorland Gazette
29. Borough Treasurer of Kendal
30. G. Abraham
31. George Romney (Portrait of Captain Rbt Banks — Abbot Hall Gallery)
32. Wainwright's
33. Wordsworth's
34. Beatrix Potter's
35. Melvyn Bragg's
36. First to climb Nape's Needle
37. Fish Inn
38. Bigamously married her
39. Hanged in Carlisle
40. Caldbeck churchyard
41. Whitehaven
42. John Wyatt, formerly Chief Ranger, NP.
43. Dorothy Wordsworth
44. Ruskin
45. Beatrix Potter
46. Melvyn Bragg
47. Lord Whitelaw
48. Bishop of Carlisle
49. Lord Lonsdale
50. A. Wainwright

Section Nine: **Sports**

1. Cumberland & Westmorland Wrestling at Grasmere
2. Blencathra, Melbreak, Ullswater, Eskdale & Ennerdale, Coniston, Lunesdale
3. Grasmere Sports
4. Horse Sales
5. Ambleside, Grasmere, Musgrave, Urswick, Warcop
6. c
7. Grotesque faces
8. Biggest Liar Competition
9. Fell running
10. Fox hunting — he was Huntsman of the Ullswater
11. c
12. Driving horses — at Lowther Horse Trials
13. Yes — season 1974-75
14. Brunton Park
15. No horses; no red coats for the members — they hunt on foot
16. Grey
17. Aniseed soaked cloth
18. Char
19. Spain
20. Eat their own wool — for the wool content
21. No mortar or cement between the stones
22. Allowed to live wild on the fells
23. Counting — one, two, three
24. a Last year's lamb
    b a male sheep
    c a yearling sheep
25. a Clearing b waterfall
    c island d small hill
    e narrow ravine f narrow pass
    g projecting spur h peak
    i gap in a ridge
26. Century
27. Grizedale
28. Bowness
29. Mint cake
30. Cumbrian Publications
31. Sports goods
32. Supermarket
33. Climbing clothes
34. Books
35. Old books
36. Supermarket
37. Paintings
38. Printing
39. Estate agents
40. Time sharing companies
41. Bus Co.
42. Coach Hire Co.
43. Barrovian
44. Keswickian
45. Grasmerian
46. Cockermouthian
47. Kendalian
48. Westmerian
49. Carliol
50. Penrithan

Section Ten: **Fun**

1 b
2 c
3 b
4 c
5 b
6 c
7 c, d, f
8 c
9 c
10 a
11 a
12 Great Cockup
13 Askham
14 Caldbeck
15 Boot
16 Catbells
17 Crinkle Crags
18 Friar's Crag
19 Great Gable
20 Hardknott
21 High Spy
22 Because of the Furness
23 Howtown
24 Ireby
25 Loweswater
26 The Old Man
27 Styhead tarn
28 Swindale

29 Aira Force
30 Flookburgh
31 Keswick
32 Ullswater
33 Carlisle
34 Bowness
35 Buttermere
36-41 I'm too tired. Please correct your own.
42 Kendal
43 Barrow
44 Penrith
45 Keswick
46 b
47 c
48 a
49 a
50 b
51 Alcock, Ambleside, Armboth, Barrow, Beckfoot, Borrowdale, Buttermere, Carrock, Dalemain, Dearham, Kirkstone, Loadpot, Maryport, Saddleback, Seascale, Townend, Whitehaven, Wrynose
52 & 53 Check it yourself

54 Crossword Solution

ACROSS

1 — Tilberthwaite
9 — Rogue
10 — Ennerdale
12 — Fleetwith
13 — Forge
14 — Tool-bag
16 — Shrimps
18 — Sadgill
20 — Spelter
22 — Label
24 — Dalegarth
26 — Glaramara
27 — Elate
28 — Brotherswater

DOWN

2 — Inglewood
3 — Bleat
4 — Reefing
5 — Hunches
6 — Aira Force
7 — Profit
8 — Levens
11 — Air
15 — Brilliant
17 — Miterdale
18 — Silage
19 — Ludgate
20 — Salaams
21 — Reheel
23 — Baa
25 — Greta